the truth
& other stories

John,
on the day of the
poets' workshop, Apr. 14, 1973

Terry

the truth

& other stories

terrence heath

anansi

toronto

1972

Copyright © the author, 1972.

Cover design by Hilary Norman.
Cover photo by Greg Plosz.

House of Anansi Press,
471 Jarvis Street,
Toronto, Canada.

Library of Congress Card Number: 72-83485.
ISBN: 0 88784 323 9 (paper) 0 88784 422 7 (cloth).

Printed in Canada by The Hunter Rose Company.

72 73 74 75   4 3 2 1

To R. E. Rashley

table of contents

the frogs

the frogs could be found about fifty feet downstream
from the hard bank of the place in the creek which
the boys used as a swimming hole.   the ground at
the swimming hole was fairly even about three feet
above the water.   where the frogs sat the ground sank
sharply down to water level.   coarse bright grass
grew around the frogs and the ground had a salty
crust in some places.   the frogs were not large.   the
largest would have been no longer than two inches.
they were not hard to catch.   three boys could
collect a dozen in ten minutes.   once the frogs were
caught the boys usually let them go again.
occasionally the frogs were killed.   a fourth boy
showed them something else that could be done with
the frogs.   he found a good stand of brome grass
back from the swimming hole and selected four large
stalks.   he broke the stalks off near the nodules and
brought the four hollow grass stalks back to the bank.
he gave each boy a stalk and kept one for himself.
the stalks were dry and brittle.   he took a frog in his
left hand, closing his hand over its head and exposing
the back end of the frog.   he used the end of the
grass stalk to find the frog's asshole and then inserted
the stalk.   when the stalk was in about half an inch
he took the other end in his mouth and started to
blow, releasing his grip on the frog slowly.   the frog
began to expand until it was almost a perfect sphere.
it could be put down safely then because its feet did

not reach the ground.   each boy blew up a frog.
they did a second round and a third.   the fourth
boy picked up two frogs and gently placed them in
the creek.   they floated off downstream, turning
and spinning on the water.   when all twelve were
launched the boys threw stones and exploded them.

the mother

between the shoulder and the elbow her arm had a layer of fat under the skin. about one third of the way between the shoulder and the elbow on the outside of the arm there was a red mark which was not a pimple. the back of the arm was white and smooth. there was a horizontal dimple just above the elbow. under the skin at the back, dark blue veins showed through. they were not distinct. further under the arm at the top was the hollow of the armpit. the hollow was large and the skin wrinkled. the brown hair in the armpit was curly except for some of the ends. the inside of the arm was also white but not as smooth as the back.

when the boy lay beside his mother in bed he placed his cheek on the back of her arm at the top. the skin was cool and smooth. he held her arm tightly against his cheek until the spot was warm. then he moved his cheek down to a new, cool place. when that spot was warm he moved his cheek further down to a new cool place. when he reached the elbow he moved to the top which was now cool again.

3

the brown dog

in front of the three boys the dry thin prairie grass
parted as the toes of their running shoes pressed on
the clumps of stems.   the boys were well away from
the road at the exact centre on the circle of prairie.
their voices were lost in the heat and wind.   the boy
at the right carried a shingle arrow rubber and a
handful of shingle arrows.   each arrow had a
finishing nail driven into its tip.

three-quarters of a mile from the road and a mile
from the railway tracks at the edge of what was once
a cultivated piece of land lay the brown dog.   it was
very big, enough boxer in it to be called a boxer but
much larger.   its back legs were drawn up under its
body; it seemed ready to leap.   its front feet were
extended, the paws spaced a few inches apart.   its
black muzzle rested on its front paws and was the
only part of the dog that seemed relaxed.   its eyes
were lost in the folds of black skin over the sockets
or else they were closed.   flies walked over the
creased skin on its shoulders.   the skin did not twitch
or shudder.   the hairs lay individually short and flat
over the skin.

the boys stopped.   the flies moved their bodies,
rubbed legs together, walked over the dog's hair.   one
fly buzzed around the boys.   the shingle arrow rubber
hung slack beside the boy's trouser leg.   their

4

breathing moved the stripes on the boys' T-shirts.
the boy in the middle shifted his weight.   the prairie
grass bent under his running shoes.   the dog lay still.

about ten feet separated the three boys from the dog.
behind it and behind them was the prairie.   a whisper.
let's get outta here.   no one moved.   the flies rubbed
legs together, walked over the dog's hair.   another
whisper.   here doggie here doggie.   the dog lay still.
the boy in the middle took three half-steps toward
the dog.   the flies moved.   three more half-steps.
here doggie.   the boy on the left followed.   then the
third boy.   whisper.   is he dead?   the boy in the lead
walked forward until his foot stopped just in front of
the dog's nose.   flies rose into the air.   the dog's
head lay on its front paws.   the boy stepped closer.
he placed his foot on the dog's shoulder.   pushed.
the body rolled onto its left side.   the head fell
heavily backwards.   one boy pointed to the marks on
the dog's throat.

maggots burrowed in the short brown hair.

the strip

the branches of the carragana hedge were silver-green.
the leaves were dark green. the pods were yellow
with a brown rib curling up to a point at the end of
each one. the girl stood between the hedge and the
four boys.

she reached back behind her neck and unbuttoned
the top two buttons of her dress. she lowered her
arms and reached back behind her waist and
unbuttoned the bottom two. she moved both
shoulders forward. the dress slid down her arms.
she took her arms out of the sleeves. the dress fell
to her bare feet. she stepped out of the dress, bent
down, picked it up and hung it on the carragana
hedge. she held the sleevehole of her cotton
undershirt with her right hand and pulled her left
elbow and arm into her shirt. she stuck her hand
down and raised her undershirt to her shoulder. she
held the other sleevehole of her undershirt with her
left hand and pulled back her right elbow and arm
into her shirt. she stuck her hand down and raised
her undershirt to her shoulder. she took the
undershirt in both hands and pushed it up over her
head. she hung it on the carragana hedge next to her
dress. she hooked her thumbs in the elastic band at
the top of her cotton panties and pushed the panties
down her legs. she raised the right leg out of the
panties. then the left leg. she picked up the panties

and hung them on the carragana hedge.

the arms, head and legs were brown.   the torso was
white and almost rectangular.   around the waist was
a slight roll of fat.   the chest also had a layer of fat.
the small pink nipples stuck out.   at the bottom of
the torso at the front was a short vertical crack about
an inch long.

there, now give me the nickels.

the basement

on the north side of the basement the prairie went
out in a flat semi-circle to the horizon. about twenty
feet to the south of the cement walls the last dirt
street ran along the prairie. two houses stood across
the street from the basement. near this basement
was a second but the boys did not use it.

the boys stood inside the rectangle of cement walls.
only one wall had an unbroken flat top. the others
were partly caved in. the window holes were
three-sided and had weeds growing in them. the
walls were cold. large stones showed through the
surface of the rough grey cement. slabs of concrete
lay on the ground. most of them had one or two
sides squared off. the other sides were uneven. they
were half buried. once the boys found a bent spoon
buried in the dirt.

the knock-out

a group of boys stood around two boys in the school
basement.   a big boy stood behind a smaller one and
put his arms under the arms and around the stomach
of the smaller boy.

i'll count to ten.   at each count take a deep breath
and i'll squeeze.   it won't hurt.

the smaller boy pulled at the hands around his waist
but he could not get them unclasped.

be a sport.   it won't hurt.   one.

the smaller boy drew in his stomach and the big boy
squeezed.

two.

the smaller boy took another deep breath.

three.   four.   five.

the smaller boy pulled at the hands.

look, it doesn't hurt does it?   that's all there is to it.
six.   seven.   eight.   nine.   ten.

the big boy released his hold and stepped back.   the

smaller boy stood in the centre of the ring of boys. his face was white.   he fell slowly forward into the ring of boys onto the cement floor of the basement.

let's get outta here.

the tongue

at the back of the house a man and two boys stood
near a chicken-wire cage.   the man held a crow in his
left hand.   his fingers were closed over the wings and
his thumb held the crow's legs back.   his hand was
high up on the crow's back and he held the crow's
beak open by putting the tip of his index finger
between the upper and lower parts of the beak.   the
crow's tongue was pointed.   the man held a razor
blade between the thumb and index finger of his
right hand.

his left hand closed more tightly on the crow.   he
placed one corner of the razor blade about a quarter
of an inch in from the tip of the crow's tongue and
pressed down.   the blade went through the tongue.
the tongue then had two points.   the man put the
razor into his vest pocket, opened the door of the
cage and put the crow inside.   the crow hopped over
to the far corner.   he blinked his eyes.   the man
closed the door of the cage and fastened it with a
bent nail.

now he'll talk.

the chinaman

the chinaman visited his greenhouses three mornings
a week, tuesday, thursday, saturday. he had three
houses of glass — roof and walls — standing beside
one another facing east and west. a fourth house had
stood in the row on the north side. all that remained
of it were the rotting foundation boards. the glass
had been used to repair the broken windows of the
other three houses. the houses were all alike, about
nine feet high in the middle, the roofs slanting down
to the three foot walls. at the east end of each house
was a wooden door. the doors were locked with
combination padlocks. the dials of the locks were
black in the centre with white numbers and lines
radiating out to the circumference of the dial. there
were rust spots on the metal.

three boys walked across the prairie behind the houses
until they reached the place where the fourth house
had stood. it was thursday afternoon, about three.
they stepped over the rotting foundation board out of
the dry prairie grass into the rectangle of dirt, weeds,
trampled ground. near the third greenhouse the
earth was moist. the three boys bent over and moved
slowly toward the east, picking up things from the
ground — glass, nails, boards, hinges — throwing them
down again. halfway along the side of the rectangle
one boy gave a yell for the others to come. he held
up some newspapers. they seemed to be comics.

over them they had neat columns of ideograms.   the
boys looked at each paper carefully, page by page.
the chinaman came around the corner at the east
end.   he held a knife in one hand.   it was about
twelve inches long, with a dark brown handle.   he
shouted and waved his knife.

the boys stood looking at him.   he shouted again.
they ran.   one fell, crawled, stumbled to his feet,
ran.   he was crying.   the three boys ran out onto the
prairie.   the chinaman threw his knife.   it stuck in
one of the rotting foundation boards.

the erection

the big boy seated himself in the back of the round
hut of carragana bushes. the six smaller boys sat in
a semi-circle facing him. the big boy undid the
buttons of his jeans, reached into the opening and
pulled out his penis. it was large and white. in his
hand it grew larger until it stood straight up. he
reached into his back pocket and brought out a
square of cardboard which had creases in it in one
direction and was curled. he made a cylinder of it
and fitted it over his upright penis. the head of the
penis stuck out the end of the cylinder. it was
blue-nosed and the split was slightly open. he began
to move the cardboard cylinder slowly up and down.
each time the cylinder came down the head of the
penis showed. he moved the cardboard up and down
faster. he stopped. the semen squirted into the air
and landed in the middle of the semi-circle of boys.

14

the post

the post was rotting at the bottom.   its crumbling
centre was visible beneath the brown-grey surface of
the wood.   a definite dark brown ring marked off the
rotting part from the grey wood of the top part of
the post.   the post stood in a cowyard.   it leaned.
it did not line up with any other posts.   near the
post was a footpath that led to the iron bridge across
the creek.   every day at about four-fifteen the boys
walked along the path from the school to the creek.
on saturdays and during the summer holidays they
came at almost anytime during the morning or
afternoon.   when they came to the post they each
fumbled with the metal buttons stamped GWG,
found the slit in the underwear, plucked out the penis
between thumb and first finger and sent wobbling
arcs of urine over the base of the post.   while peeing
they side-stepped around the post in order to ensure
an even and thorough wetting.   by late june the dark
ring was clearly defined and the wood brown.   in mid
august the boys' interest waned even though the
wood had become darker and more pitted.   it was the
following spring that they noticed the rot.

the strap

seven boys out of the fifty who had been involved in
the snowball fight stood along the hallway in a
straight line with their right hands extended.   the
vice-principal moved slowly down the line, raising
the black strap in an arc at each boy and bringing it
down on the outstretched hand.   hold it out straight.
the black strap arced and fell.   a strip of skin
reddened on each palm after the strap hit.   when the
vice-principal reached the seventh boy he returned
to the first.   now the left hand.   the black strap rose
in its arc and fell.   the skin reddened.   the
vice-principal side-stepped down the hall.   when he
reached the seventh boy, he stopped and came back
to the first again.   the right hand again.   don't cup
it.   the black strap rose and fell, rose and fell.   the
redness spread over the entire surface of the hands.
one boy started to cry.   the hall was empty.   his
tears fell on the brown speckled tile floor.   no one
noticed.   the vice-principal reached the seventh boy,
turned and walked back down the line to the first
boy.   now the left.   the black strap arced up and
down.   one boy jerked his hand back.   the strap hit
his fingertips.   hold it out.   all the way.   the black
strap fell again.   when the vice-principal came to the
seventh boy, he turned and came back to the first.
now the right hand.   the black strap rose in an arc
and fell.   all the way out.   the vice-principal
side-stepped down the line.   no.   hold it out.

16

when the vice-principal reached the seventh boy he
returned down the line to the first. now the left
hand. the black strap arced up and down. the hands
were swelling and the redness had spread along the
edges of the fingers. when the vice-principal reached
the seventh boy he turned and walked back to the
first. the right. the black strap rose in an arc and
fell. when the vice-principal came to the seventh boy
he returned to the first. hold out the left hand. all
the way out. the black strap rose and fell in arcs.
three of the boys were weeping now. the
vice-principal side-stepped down the line. when he
came to the seventh boy he turned and walked back
to the office with the sign VICE-PRINCIPAL over
the door.

the witch

mrs. schmidt and the boy stepped down from the
backporch of the house onto the prairie.   they
followed two ruts toward the railroad yard.   grey
dust rose around their feet.   when they reached
the tracks they walked along the timbers and picked
up pieces of coal until her basket was almost full.
they turned towards her house again and walked
diagonally across the prairie.   every few steps she
pointed to the ground and the boy bent down and
found the plants she meant.   some of the plants he
dug out by the roots.   from some he picked the
leaves, from some the flowers.   the coal could no
longer be seen through the green plants in the basket.
they reached the framed rectangular screendoor at
the back of her house.

one moment.   i have something for you.   she went
into the house.   the coiled spring on the door
stretched open and closed again.   it had worn a
smooth groove in the side of the wood.   the boy
stood in the wild portulaca near the back door.   he
moved his feet; they raised dust in the air.   he could
not see into the house.

she came to the door.   the coiled spring opened and
closed.   in her right hand was a black box.

here.   a camera.   for you.   now you can take pictures.

the shingle arrow gun

the materials needed are a short round stick at least a
half inch thick and preferably of willow wood. a
strip of inner tube approximately seven inches long
and three-quarters of an inch wide. a piece of
butcher's cord. a supply of old shingles and finishing
nails.

cut a notch the width of the rubber about one-quarter
of an inch from one end of the willow stick. lay the
rubber on top of the notch when stick is held in left
hand and wrap it around the stick and hold it along
the main length of rubber. place the stick on the
ground with the rubber wrapped around and hold it
there with one foot. with the left hand stretch the
short end of rubber pressed against the main length of
rubber and tie the butcher cord around both pieces of
rubber close to the stick. out of the remainder of
the butcher cord make a loop about one inch in
diameter and tie it to the other end of the rubber.

the shingle arrow gun is ready.

to make the arrows cut shingle strips approximately
one inch wide and the full length of the shingles.
you will need at least one half dozen of these. hold
the strip of shingle on its edge and begin to cut at a
slant across the grain about one and a half inches
from each end. do not pry out the long middle piece

until the end cuts are equally deep. a shaft of
shingle about a half inch wide or less should remain
between the heavy head end and light tail of the
arrow. round off the corners of the head to decrease
its wind resistance. about an inch from the end of
the head on the side opposite the shaft cut a notch
at an angle into the side of the head. this notch
must be deep enough to hold the string and smooth
so that the string is released easily. hammer a small
finishing nail into the end of the head of each arrow.

to shoot hold the gun horizontally in the left hand.
the fingers curling over the top of the stick to form a
fist. the thumb stretched out horizontally along the
stick pointing toward the rubber. the rubber should
lie smoothly over the top of the stick and hang over
between the stick and yourself with the loop dangling.
hook an arrow in the dangling loop. hold the tail of
the arrow between the thumb and first finger of the
right hand. raise the arrow to a horizontal position
with the notch in which the string is hooked at the
bottom. twist the gun away from you one half turn.
pull the arrow back as far as possible. bring to eye
level. aim quite high above the target and release.

the hunters

the two boys walked crouched over with their knees
bent. they went between the shrubs and trees near
the river. the boy in front carried a bow and arrow.
the other boy carried a knapsack. the boy in front
held the arrow in the notch of the bow with one
hand. the other hand hung down at his side. he
stopped and raised his hand. the boy behind stopped
too. the boy in front pointed to a brown shape on
the other side of a small bluff. the shape moved.
the boy in front placed his free hand on the end of
the arrow and drew the arrow back about an inch
and a half. the boys moved forward slowly. when
they reached the edge of the bluff about forty feet
from the shape, the boy in front stopped, stood up
and began to pull back the end of the arrow and the
string of the bow. when he had it back as far as he
could pull it, he moved the bow and arrow first to
one side and then to the other. he raised them
slightly. the other boy watched. then the boy in
front lowered the bow until the arrow pointed to the
ground at his feet. he let the string down slowly
until it was straight across the bow again.

what's wrong?

shhh. come on.

the first boy put the arrow in his belt and slung the

bow over his shoulder.   he went down onto his knees
and started to crawl into the bluff.   the second boy
knelt down and crawled after him.   the brown shape
on the other side of the bluff was moving up and
down.   when they got to the other side of the bluff,
the boys lay down and looked through the grass and
brush.   at the other end of the brown shape were the
heads of a man and a woman.

the balloons

the five boys found the balloons along the bicycle
trail around the lake.   they were large balloons about
four inches long and three-quarters of an inch wide.
they were cream-coloured.   they were not good for
blowing up.   the boys took them to a stand pipe and
filled them with water.   they held a lot of water.
when they had filled a dozen or more balloons, they
divided into two teams with three on one side and
two on the other.   they each took two or three
balloons.   two boys stood on the planking around the
stand pipe.   the other three boys spread out around
the stand pipe.   when they were about ten feet away,
the boys threw the balloons at the boys on the
planking of the stand pipe.   several of the balloons
hit the stand pipe and planking and broke.   one broke
on the pant leg of a boy on the planking.   the others
hit the ground near the stand pipe.   when the three
boys had no more balloons left, the boys on the
planking jumped down and broke their balloons on
the backs of the other boys as they ran away.

the collection

i'll give you three hockey players for no. 3 of the animals.

no.

why not? what's so hot about a triceratop anyhow?

you ever see no. 3 before? i know a boy's got all the sports cards. but i don't know anyone with this card.

ah, lots of kids have it.

i never seen it.

look, i'll give you this destroyer and pt boat too.

they're your doubles. i only got one of these. nobody else's ever got it and you want to give me your lousy doubles.

o.k. i'll give you all the sports cards i got.

is it alla them?

no, but almost. i'll give you my doubles too. there's lots there you don't have.

well. all for this no. 3? why you want this card

so bad?

i got all the animals but that one.

let's see.

see. 1,2,4,5, alla them.

yah.   what if there's only one of these ever made?

they wouldn't do that.   there's lotsa them.

yah?   well, i want to keep it.

you haven't even got all the other animals.   what you
goin to do with it anyway?

i dunno.   just keep it.

the voice

all the girls and boys in the grade four and five classes
were standing in three rows in a semi-circle on the
stage. a black piano stood to the right of them.
Miss Morland sat on the round piano stool. Miss
Pughes stood in front of the boys and girls. Miss
Pughes raised her hand and Miss Morland began to
sing, "among the leaves so green-o". as they sang
Miss Pughes moved her hand through the air.
she walked along the front row of girls. listened.
moved her hand. when she reached the end of the
row she walked back to the second row of girls and
small boys. listened. at the end of the row she
turned. moved her hand and walked down the back
row of boys. she paused in front of the third boy
from the left end. sing up. she raised her hand and
brought it down. everyone stopped singing. you
can just move your lips during the recital. the piano
began again. she walked on down the row.

the hard

put your hand in my pocket.

why?

oh, come on. do it.

i don't want to.

you scared or somethin?   come on, it's a surprise.

i don't want no surprises. if it's a surprise why don't
you bring it out.

won't come out.

whatta ya mean, it won't come out?

put your hand in and you'll see.   it won't come out.

it's probably a turtle or somethin that bites.

cross my heart and hope to die, it ain't somethin that
bites.   it won't hurt ya.   honest to god.

well.

the boy put his hand into the other boy's front right

hand pocket.   at the bottom of the pocket he felt a
large warm penis under the cloth.   it throbbed.

i'm gonna tell the teacher.

go ahead.   she can put her hand in too.

the swimming trunks

the boy's hand that grabbed the wet wool swimming
trunks from the bank of the creek was large and
chapped. the fingernails bulged along the centre and
ended in a thin dirty line above the quick.   the
knuckles had several red brown scabs and cracks.   the
hand perhaps seemed larger because it came at the
end of a skinny wrist and arm.   the boy attached to
the arm laughed and threw the dripping trunks out
into the middle of the swimming hole.   the other
boys laughed as they walked away over a small dam
across the creek.

the boy the trunks belonged to was already dressed
and didn't laugh.   it was late afternoon.   he took off
his clothes, left them in a small conical heap and
walked the three or four steps to the edge of the
water.   his shoulder blades disappeared as he took a
breath and dived in.   he came up, blowing water.   he
dived again.   each time his body surfaced, the water
fanned out in concentric circles.   he dived.   surfaced.
dived.   surfaced again.   the globules of water
glistened on arms and shoulders.   he breathed hard
and irregularly.   he looked around and dived again.
came to the surface and swam to shore.   crawled
onto the hard mud bank.   the water surface flattened
out.   the boy turned his body, got to his feet and
put on his clothes.   he put his socks into his running
shoes, picked up the shoes by the laces and walked

along the bank, over the dam across the creek and up the path that disappeared towards the road.

the icehouse

the heat pumped against the boys' faces and chests.
black smoke bulged up in layers. flames stood
upright from the walls. four men stood at one end
of the building and watched the fire and smoke. the
boys stood at the side. the building was burnt down
further on their side than at the end. inside the
wooden walls was a wall of straw. it was not
burning. it was brown-yellow. inside the straw
the edges of large blocks of ice could be seen.
at the top, the blocks were rounded off and clear.
lower down, the edges were sharp and the ice was
cloudy. the cracks between the layers were distinct.
as the boys watched the blocks of ice on top sank.
they could not see where the water from the ice went.
the wooden wall sank more quickly than the ice wall.
the wall of straw sank with the ice.

the fire had started to burn the brown grass around
the foundation of the building when the firetruck
arrived. the men in firemen's uniforms climbed
down from the truck and unrolled a black hose.
when a fireman held it toward the building the water
started to come out. the stream of water ran down
between the wooden walls and the straw and along
the cracks between the ice blocks. the sun shone
on the black smoke.

the filling

just before the 4 o'clock bell, the brown roll squeezed
out his asshole into the curled interior fleece of his
winter underwear.   when the tip of the roll came
down against the underwear it turned and pushed
between the boy's legs and into the space at the back
of his pants.   the boy pushed himself against the
desk.   the tip of the brown roll began to flatten in
the angle between the seat and the desk back.   the
roll was being squeezed into a flat patty.   the patty
spread out onto both cheeks of the boy's bum.   the
brown roll moved out soundlessly in rhythmic but
irregular thrusts.   when the boy leaned back, it came
out more slowly.

the bell rang.

the boys and girls stood up in rows on the right hand
sides of their desks.   the rows beginning with the row
closest to the window moved forward one after the
other.   the rows walked to the front of the room,
turned a right angle and walked out the door.
outside the door the room monitor for the week
swung his newspaper bag at the boys in the line.   the
row the boy was in was the sixth row from the
window.   when the sixth row began to move forward,
the boy walked forward in short steps with his legs
apart.   the row turned a right angle and went out
the door at the front of the classroom.   the patty

fell down into the flap of the underwear but
remained attached at the hole.   then it came loose
and lay cradled in the crotch of his underwear.

the room monitor stood outside the door and swung
his paper bag at the boys in the line.   the bag rose,
swung forward and hit the patty hard up between the
boy's legs.   with his legs apart the boy ran down the
hall.

the aunt

she stood behind him and held his head in her two
hands.   as she moved her fingers in his hair, a white
lather began to appear.   it ran down his forehead
into the corners of his eyes and in streams along both
sides of his nose.   he held his mouth closed.   when
his head was covered with lather, she bent her fingers
and began to scratch his head with her nails.   his
hair stood up.   his cheeks and ears turned red.

aren't you goin to be beautiful.

the father

the man stood in front of the open door of the
furnace. his hands and face were red. his grey hair
was slightly pink at the front. he wore grey bib
overalls with thin black stripes down them. they had
pockets in front and back and smaller pockets on the
bib. he wore a dark grey shirt. it was buttoned at
the neck and the wrists. he wore brown leather
gloves. he walked over to the pile of coal in a bin
boarded off in the corner of the basement. at the
back of the bin there was a window hole with a
sliding board in it. the coal was piled highest under
the window. the bottom of the pile reached the
opening of the bin. a sledge hammer a shovel and a
bucket with a large spout stood outside the opening
of the coal bin. the man picked up the shovel,
pushed it along the floor under the pile of coal. he
lifted a shovelful of coal and carried it to the open
door of the furnace. he swung the shovel back and
then forward. the pieces of coal came off the end
of the shovel and flew in an arc into the furnace.
when the coal landed in the furnace, sparks came out
of the open door. the face of the man became
redder. he walked over to the coal pile, pushed the
shovel along the floor under the coal and lifted
some of the coal from the top of the pile rolled down.
he took the shovelful of coal to the open door of
the furnace and threw it in. when the coal landed in
the furnace, sparks came out the open door. he

walked over to the coal pile, pushed the shovel under
the coal and brought a shovelful of coal to the open
door of the furnace. he threw the coal in and sparks
came out the open door. he walked over to the coal
pile, pushed the shovel under the coal and lifted.
some of the coal from the top of the pile rolled down.
he carried the shovelful of coal to the open door of
the furnace and threw it in. he walked over to the
coal bin and placed the shovel against the wall near
the opening of the bin. he walked back to the
furnace and took hold of the iron bar across the door.
he closed the door and let the iron bar fall into the
notch at the side of the door. red light came out of
the holes of the grates in the front of the door and
lit up parts of the ceiling and walls of the basement.
the man closed the grates halfway. he bent down
and took hold of the iron bar on the door at the
bottom of the furnace. he lifted the iron bar out of
its notch and opened the door. he pulled out a tin
tray full of ashes. some sparks still burned red
amongst the grey and black ashes. he walked over
to the bucket near the opening of the coal bin and
tipped the tray full of ashes into the bucket. he
walked back to the furnace, put the tray into the
bottom of the furnace, took hold of the iron bar,
closed the door and let the bar fall into the notch at
the side of the door. he opened the grates in the
bottom door. the man took off his gloves and stuck

them between two boards on the side of the coal bin. he turned and walked up the stairs.

the rinkhut

the iron stove threw out a square circle of heat.   the
boy, burning the yellow spruce boards of the hut,
thrust the red poker out through the wall into the
night.   he replaced the end of the poker in the stove
and waited.   when the heat showed through the iron
again, he lifted the poker by its wooden handle and
returned to the strip of board between the two by
four studs.   the board smoked.   he had burned out a
small hole.   now he was enlarging it.   the hole had a
bulge at the bottom.   he returned the poker to the
fire and waited.   the hot iron bit into the board again.
the hole now had two fat projections at the bottom.
the boy began burning out the wood between the
projections.   he had to return the iron to the stove.
next time he started to enlarge the hole sideways.
the iron had to be replaced in the fire.   the boy stuck
three fingers out the hole.   he drew them back in.
he put his eye to the hole.   he could see nothing.
when he turned to get the poker, another boy had it
and was burning a hole in the wall on the other side
of the hut.

the caretaker

the boy found the man lying on his back on the
cement floor near the pits in front of the two steam
boilers.   the man wore black boots, dark green
trousers, a blue denim jacket, a grey shirt buttoned
at the neck.   his left leg was straight but the right
one was bent at the knee and stuck out sideways.
his grey work socks showed.   his hands were by his
sides.   on the table under the light stood a black
lunch box.   next to it, a red and grey thermos bottle.
the lid was on the table.   it was red.   the man's face
was dark grey-blue.   his lips were purple.   his eyes
were open.

the boy walked out of the furnace room and next day
the school flag flew at half mast.

the bicycle

look i got a new bike. my dad bought it for me. new.

wow. look at that. can i have a ride?

no. my dad says i'm not supposed to.

ah for christ's sake. it ain't goin to hurt it. come on. give us one little ride. just around the block.

no, honest i can't.

my dad's gonna buy me a bike too. what kinda bike is it? a Standard? my dad's buying me a CCM.

so what. this is a new bike just like a CCM.

where'd he get it? from a catalogue? look it ain't even got a chain guard. where's the chain guard, smartie?

i roll up my pant leg. you don't need a chain guard. my dad says so.

what's your dad know about bikes. he don't even have a job.

he knows lots. he's got a bike. a CCM.

bet it's an old one. why don't you turn the
handlebars around. here. like this.

don't. i don't want the handlebars up. leave them
alone.

that's the way girls have them. CCM's got two white
stripes on the frame and two red ones on the fenders.
yours only got one.

that's cause it's a Standard and Standards only got
one.

ain't you got a slapper for the back wheel? for a
motor?

my dad says that'll loosen the spokes.

your dad don't know his ass from a hole in the ground.

my dad does too. he knows. . . .he bought me this
bike. new. you ain't got no new bike.

we don't want no new Standards. we don't want no
sissies around here neither. go on. get out of here.
go play with the girls fore your father climbs out of

41

his asshole.   go on.   back to your daddy, sissy pants.

i guess i better be goin.

the boy put his foot on the pedal nearest him.   he
pushed with his other foot, raised it over the seat and
pushed down on the pedal.   one of the boys swung a
baseball bat at the fender of the bicycle and broke
the red glass in the tail light.

the dogfight

the boy's desk sat in the row closest to the windows
under the middle window.   the window was open.
the boy had a half sheet of lined foolscap on his desk.
he held a short pencil in his hand.   on the foolscap
five planes flew through the sky.   one was larger than
the rest.   a bomber.   the windows in it were
cross-hatched and guns stuck out in all directions.
it carried a series of concentric circles on its square
tail as did two of the smaller planes.   the other two
small planes had crosses on their tails.   one of these
german planes had been hit by the gunfire from one
of the british fighters and smoke came out in curlicues
from its tail.   the other german plane was climbing
straight up and the gunfire from the bomber was
reaching out in its direction.   the sky was full of
explosions and small clouds of smoke.   beneath the
planes factories and buildings burned with long flames
coming from their rooftops.   bombs still fell from
the bomber and it looked as if the german fighter
would crash into the flaming buildings.

the boy folded the piece of paper in half, opened it
out, folded the two top corners to the centre crease,
then folded the fold-over once more.   he made two
creases parallel to the centre crease.   he lifted the
sides of the folded paper until they were level.   he
held the paper by the folded part at the bottom.   he
threw the paper out the open window.

the soldier

the door of the house opened.   a man in soldier's
uniform came out and stood on the back porch.   he
put his boots down one after another on the four
steps and then onto the dirt path.   he went along
the footpath to the brown shed at the bottom of
the yard.

the roof and walls of the shed were covered with
brown shingles.   two boys were near the shed.   the
larger boy held a B-B gun in one hand.   he held it by
the barrel and the handle hung down almost to the
tops of the weeds around his feet.   the smaller boy
was kneeling on the ground.   he held his head in his
hands.   he was crying.   his tears dropped into the
dust in front of his knees and rolled up into black
balls.

when the man got to the boys, he reached out and
took the rifle from the larger boy.   the boy's hand
held onto the gun and the man had to pull hard
before the hand let go.   both boys looked at the man.

did you hit him with this?

yes.

the man held the gun with one hand at the end of the
handle and with the other hand around the end of the

barrel.   he raised it in front of him above his head.
he raised his right knee until it was level in front of
his hip.   he brought the gun down.   it broke off
just above the metal on the handle.   the wood stuck
up from the metal in long and short splinters.   the
man threw the two parts of the gun down in the dust
and walked back to the porch.   he went into the
house.

the larger boy picked up the two pieces of gun and
tried to fit them together.   he was crying.

the sunday school lesson

god is one, unique, indivisible, unknown, in glory.
no one has ever looked on god.
god is light.
god is different from anything you know.   he is
something unlike anything you have ever seen.   there
are things you have never seen.   i can show you
something you have never seen before and will never
see again.   do you believe that?

he took a peanut out of his pocket and cracked it
open. he showed the boys and girls the two nuts.
one was light brown.   the thin skin of the second
was missing on top and the white-yellow flesh showed
through.   the two nuts rested in half of the shell
which was much smoother inside than out.

you have never seen these before.

he turned the half shell over.   the two nuts rolled into
the palm of his other hand.   he put his hand
open-palmed up to his mouth.   the nuts rolled into
his mouth and he chewed them.   he swallowed the
pulp.

and you will never see them again.

the truants

the two boys lay side by side between the skids of
the boardwalk.   above them they could see a thin
rectangle of sky between two crossplanks.   the
carragana hedge of the school grounds rose vertically
at the north end of the rectangle.   then the long slit
of blue.   the planks were brown and stained
underneath.   at the top of the crack grey slivers
frayed the straight edges of the rectangle.   the sun
shone through onto the boys.   a strip of light ran
over the ground and the boys' chests, another over
their waists, another above their knees and another on
their shins.   the next strip stretched smoothly across
the ground.

the footsteps of the two teachers returning from
lunch made a steady beat the length of the boardwalk.
as the footfalls approached the boys lay still. they
watched the soles of the shoes step on the crack
above their faces.   they could see part of the legs.
dirt fell down onto their mouths.   the strip of blue
sky was clear.

the fart

the two boys walked along the path between the cows until they came to the horse.   the horse's tail swatted back and forth over its rump.   the horse was fat and glossy.   the tail raised.   the two halves of the horse's backside swelled out from its flanks and came together in a trough immediately below the tail.   in the trough there was no hair.   the skin was dark grey and extended up and along the underside of the tail. the asshole was deep and set in at the base of the tail.   a slit started just below the hole and extended about six inches down the trough.   the skin along the slit was loose and stood out slightly at the bottom. as the boys watched, the skin around the asshole began to swell.   when it was tight the inner edge of the hole thrust out and opened.   for a moment the white and pink skin inside the hole was exposed, then the dark grey skin was drawn back in, until the asshole was puckered around the edges.   the puckering drew up the skin along the slit until it was tight and the protruding part at the bottom turned up.   the skin around the hole relaxed and the horse covered the hole with its tail.

the strawberries

the strawberries grew in the ditch on the south side of
the dirt road between seventh and eighth avenues on
connaught street. the berries were three-eighths of
an inch to one-quarter of an inch at their widest.
they could be found under the leaves of the plants.
there were usually two or three berries on a plant.
the plants grew amongst grass and dandelions.   the
berries got bright red in june before the end of school.
along the length of the block there were usually a
handful of berries ripe at one time.   the plants only
bore fruit for about a week.   the skins of the berries
were shiny and smooth.   the berries were easily
crushed.   they left a bright red stain on the fingers.
even if they were carried carefully in the palm of the
hand, the bottom berries were pulp after five or ten
minutes.   if they were not picked, they turned
grey-red and the skins became soft and sunken.

the mountie

two grey gym mats lay side by side on the floor of
the auditorium.   on one mat stood a boy.   the boy's
moccasins were the same colour as the gym mat.   the
laces of the left moccasin hung down.   at the bottom
of his breeches his grey socks were rolled down over
the tops of his moccasins.   at the top of his breeches
the upper part of the boy's long winter underwear
was rolled into a tube and knotted with the arms at
the front.   the boy's belly and chest were white.

on the other mat stood a man.   he wore white
running shoes over his grey socks.   his trousers were
brown with a yellow stripe about one inch wide
running down the outside of each leg.   there was a
black belt around the waist of the trousers.   he wore
a white undershirt with short sleeves.   the black hair
under his arm showed at the back of the sleevehole.

eight boys stood around the gym mats.

both the boy and the man wore large brown boxing
gloves.   the boy held his gloves together close to his
chest.   the man held his left glove close to his chest
and held the right glove out at the level of the boy's
face.   the man's arm slanted downwards.   the man
extended his right glove towards the boy's face.   the
boy raised his gloves in front of his face.   the man
drew back his right glove and extended the left

50

glove under the boy's gloves.   the boy bent over and
stumbled back a step.   when he stood up there was a
round red spot at the bottom of his ribs on the right
side.   the boy crouched down and placed his right
glove in front of his face and his left glove out further.
the right glove of the man stretched out at the level
of the boy's stomach.   the boy dropped his gloves.
the man drew back his right glove and extended his
left glove above the boy's gloves.   the boy stumbled
back a few steps and held his face in the palms of his
gloves.   he took them away.   there was a red spot
along the side of his jaw.   he was crying.

the boy crouched and ran at the man.   the man went
up on his toes, held his left glove close to his chest
and extended his right glove.   the boy ran into the
man's right glove and fell back onto the gym mat.
the man came and extended both gloves toward the
boy.   he placed one glove on each side of the boy's
chest and lifted.   when the boy was on his feet,
he hit the mountie in the face with his left glove.

the fight

since you will not do as i have asked i am going to
have to call in the vice-principal.

no, you're not.

the boy and the woman ran for the door. the boy
reached it and placed himself in front of the pebbled
glass window. the teacher stopped. she picked up
a yardstick from the blackboard ledge. she raised
it. the boy seized it with both hands. the teacher
held on. the ruler twisted back and forth, describing
half circles above the heads of the boys and girls in
the front row. the boy pushed the teacher back to
her desk, then wrenched the ruler away from her.

you're not going to tell.

he raised the ruler. she leaned back.

are you?

she put her face in her hands and started to sob.

are you?

no.

the boy stood a moment, put the ruler back on the

52

ledge and went to his seat.   the teacher cried until the recess bell rang.

the tail

the two boys carried pails of water from the slough
to the slight hill where the gopher holes were. they
poured the water down into one of the holes. as
soon as they emptied the pail they went back to the
slough and got another pailful. the third boy
squatted at the hole about ten feet from where the
boys were pouring the water. he held a piece of two
by four in his hands, resting it against his right
shoulder.

here it comes.

the two boys poured the last pails into the hole,
picked up two large rocks and ran to the other boy.
the third boy was looking down the hole. he held
the board above his head. the water was up in the
hole. a wet head came through the surface of the
water. the boy yelled and swung the board down.
he raised it again. the other two boys lifted their
rocks and threw them into the hole. the boy
dropped the two by four, bent down and put his
hand down the hole. he lifted out the body of the
gopher. its head was red and broken.

the boy took it by the tail and swung it at the end of
his arm. he jerked his arm and the body of the
gopher rose into the sky and travelled in a high half

circle before it hit the prairie.   the tail stayed in
the boy's hand.

it was worth two cents.

the truth

where's gordie?

he was not here last sunday and now he's not here
again. does anyone know if he is sick? you, you're
a friend of his, aren't you? where is he? please
speak up, even god couldn't hear that whisper. you
don't know? that's a lie, isn't it? you are lying in
church, in front of god. god hears you. you know
that don't you? do you think what you are doing is
good? don't you think god knows where gordie is?
that's false friendship. if you tell lies to cover up for
gordie, it's the same thing as playing hooky yourself.
yes it is. you might as well be out there playing ball
or whatever with him as being here telling lies. do
you understand?

now, where's gordie?

still no answer? oh i know he's a sly one. he always
smiles and seems so willing to do things. but
underneath it all he's a sneak. a wolf in lamb's
clothing. that's the devil's work. do you want to do
the devil's work too? well then. tell me where your
friend gordie has gone off to this morning. to play
ball? swim? i suppose he took his collection with
him, didn't he? eh? you have it? did he say to put
it in the collection plate? so you still have some
sense of good and bad.

56

now, where's gordie?

you might as well tell me. where did he go?   I know
he's not home sick so what is there to hide?   come
on, tell me.   it will make you feel better if you tell.
god doesn't reward liars you know.   you know that?
don't you?   god rewards the just.   remember?   for
god so loved the world that he gave his only begotten
son that whosoever believeth in him shall not die but
have everlasting life.   john 3:16.   you don't think
everlasting life is for sneaks and liars, do you?   it's
for those that tell the truth.   don't you want
everlasting life?   well, then.   tell me where gordie is.
he's out playing ball, isn't he?

sit still.   where is gordie?   listen carefully. i want you
to tell me where gordie is right now or i'm going to
have to tell your mother of your behaviour.   you
don't want me to do that do you?   your mother will
not be very happy to learn that her son is a liar, will
she?   at the school playing ball, eh?   i thought so.
now that wasn't so hard was it?   you've told the
truth.   god loves you.

the police

five men in red jackets and blue trousers with yellow
stripes down the outside of the trouser legs sat on
brown horses at the end of the field. in their right
hands they held long lances with silver points. the
points of the lances almost touched the ground near
the horses' front feet. the other end of the lances
stuck out behind the elbows of the men. in front of
each man and horse was a straight line of stakes
sticking up at regular intervals. at the end of the
lines of stakes and about seventy five feet from the
horsemen sat five loaves of white bread on the ground

a whistle blew. the five horses started to gallop
down the field beside the stakes. the men raised the
lances. as they got close to the loaves of bread, they
lowered the lances, stuck them through the loaves of
bread, lifted the bread into the air above the horses'
heads, turned the horses around and galloped back to
the end of the field.

the crowd cheered.

the theologue

the five boys stood around the man on the landing of
the stairs.   they wore 3-C badges (clean hands, clean
thoughts, clean hearts) on their jackets.

come on.   let's have some fun now.   i'll take on all
five of you at once.

one boy got behind the man.   he took a run and
jumped on the man's back.   he held on to the man's
neck and hung down.   the other four boys ran at the
man from the front and sides.   two held on to the
man's legs.   the other two held on to his arms.   the
man bent over forwards and lifted the boy on his back
high off the floor.   he reached down and unclasped
the hands of the boy holding his right leg, forced the
boy to the floor and placed his knee on the small of
the boy's back.   he reached down and unclasped the
boy's hands on his left leg, forced the boy to the floor
and placed his knee on the small of the boy's back.
the boys on the floor twisted back and forth.   their
shirts came out of their trousers.   the white skin of
the lower part of their backs showed under the man's
knees.   the man lifted his right hand and wrapped it
around the waist of the boy holding onto his right
arm.   he drew him up close to his body.   he wrapped
his left hand around the waist of the boy holding his
left arm.   he drew him up close to his body.   the
man reached over with his right hand and transferred

the boy from his left to his right side.   they twisted
and turned.   their shirts came out of their trousers.
the white skin of their backs showed under the man's
arm.   the man reached back his left hand, wrapped
his arm around the boy on his back and pulled him
to the front.   he turned him upside down.   the boy
twisted and turned.   his face was red.   his shirt and
jacket fell down over his face.   the man held him
tightly around the waist.   the boy's body began to
slip down out of his trousers.   the crack of the boy's
bum showed under the white arm muscle of the
man.   the man held the boy's body tightly.   the
boy slipped slowly to the floor.   the boy's trousers
piled up on top of the man's arm.   the man looked
at the boy.   he let the other boys go.

the honeywagon

the wagon was made of grey planking. the cracks
along the planking had a brown stain their entire
length. the stain varied in width but was wider on
the lower than on the upper plank of each join. at
about two and a half foot intervals there were
uprights outside the plank siding. these too were
grey. the brown stains along the cracks turned down
at each upright. the wagon was rounded at the
bottom and flat on top. at the back of the top was a
wooden trap door. at the back of the wagon there
was a platform made of grey planking and held up
by two iron bars attached to the sides of the wagon.
the wagon wheels were rubber. the wagon was
pulled by two horses. at the front of the wagon
high up there was a plank where two men sat. it was
not stained.

the two men wore blue bib overalls that had brown
stains on them. they wore stiff brown leather
gloves. one man had on a straw hat with a brown
stain running completely around the band. the other
man had on a green cap with a dark peak bent into a
half circle. both men wore blue shirts buttoned at
the neck with curled up collars. beneath their seat
hung two canvas bags with oats in them.

large flies hovered around the wagon. they were
especially thick along the cracks and around the edges

61

of the trap door.   when the wagon stopped at the
backhouse the two men climbed down from the seat.
the man in the straw hat climbed up onto the
platform at the back of the wagon and waited.   the
man in the green cap walked to the backhouse, opened
the door and went in.   he backed out carrying the
large galvanized pail.   he took small steps with his
legs apart.   the pail swung slowly back and forth
between his legs.   he stepped down out of the
doorway.   he set the pail down and took it in his
right hand.   he walked bent over to one side and
with shuffling steps.   the pail swung back and forth
about three inches above the ground.

when he got to the back of the wagon he set the pail
down and took the handle with two hands and lifted
it up onto the platform.   the man in the straw hat
took the handle and lifted the pail carefully onto
the top of the wagon.   he balanced it there while
opening the trap door.   he tipped it over the hole.
the brown-yellow liquid began to flow into the hole.
soaked pieces of newspaper and catalogue flowed out
in the stream.   when the pail was empty, he banged
it three times against the side of the trapdoor, set the
pail down on the platform and closed the door.   the
man in the green cap took the pail and walked to the
backhouse.   this time he walked with big steps and
swung the pail back and forth.   some of the flies

followed him.   some of the flies settled along the
cracks of the trapdoor.   the man in the straw hat
jumped to the ground, walked to the front of the
wagon and climbed up.   the man in the green
cap came out of the backhouse, closed the door and
walked to the wagon.   he reached under the seat
and took the two canvas bags with oats in them.   he
walked to the front of the horses and tied a bag onto
the halter of each horse.   he walked back to the
wagon, climbed up and sat next to the man in the
straw hat.

the coach

twelve naked boys stood around in the shower-room.
their clothes were piled on benches in front of the
steel lockers. the five showers had no curtains on
them. the coach came in. he wore black running
shoes, grey socks and a green sweat suit. around his
neck hung a silver whistle on a piece of white butcher
cord. drops of sweat stood on his forehead just
below his hairline. there was a stream of sweat down
each side of his face in front of his sideburns. black
stubble showed beneath the skin at the bottom of
his face.

he bent over and unlaced his running shoes. he took
them off. his grey socks were stuck to his feet. he
took off his socks. there was a bunch of hair at the
joint of each toe. he reached up his arms, bent them
and lifted up his sweat shirt over his head. the
whistle fell down onto his chest. across his chest and
down the centre of his belly the hair was matted and
wet. his nipples were hidden in the hair. the hair on
his shoulders and the base of his neck stood up. he
stretched the waistband of his sweat pants and pushed
them down to his ankles. he stepped out of them
and kicked them under the bench. he stretched the
waistband of his jockstrap and pulled it down over
the pouch and then down to his ankles. his penis
jumped up and then hung down. it hung in a curving
arc well below his scrotum.

he turned and farted.

the ink

the upper right hand corner of the desk held an
inkwell.   the lid was a circle with a hinge at the
back.   inside was a semi-circular glass container.   the
ink was caked on the edges of the glass.   when the
ink dried on the glass it was grey-purple.   on the pen
nib it dried black.   on skin blue.   it did not dry in
the vascula of the crocuses.   when the light purple
flowers were placed in the ink, the ink rose, dark and
distinct, up the stem past the calyx into the petals
and entered finer and finer channels until it could no
longer be seen.

the team

a boy tied a string around the penis and scrotum of
the boy standing undressed in the centre of the circle
of boys.   the boy holding the string pulled it taut.
the penis and scrotum were held out from the boy's
body in the loop of string.   another boy cut away
the pubic hair with a pair of scissors.   the black
curls of hair fell onto the varnished floor.   when the
pubic hair was cut off, the boy put the scissors down
on a bench and picked up a paint brush and a small
saucer of red tempera paint.   he painted the penis
and scrotum and the area where the pubic hair had
been.   the boy holding the string pulled and led the
boy who had been painted over to a row of three
chairs.   he held the string behind the back of the
first chair and pulled.   the undressed boy climbed
over the first chair.   the boy holding the string
pushed it under the second chair and pulled up on it
at the front.   the undressed boy crawled under the
second chair.   the boy held the string behind the
back of the third chair.   the undressed boy climbed
over the third chair.   the boy holding the string
walked around the perimeter of the basketball court.
the string held the red penis and scrotum out from
the undressed boy's body.   the undressed boy
walked behind the boy holding the string.   when
they got to the other end of the gymnasium, the boy
holding the string gave the undressed boy a sleeveless

red shirt with a number on the back. on the front
of the shirt was the name REDMEN.

the feel

the girl lay back against the couch cushions.   one foot
was on the floor.   the other knee bent along the edge
of the couch and the foot hung about two inches
above the floor.   the back of her head rested on the
padded arm of the couch.   her chin stuck up in the
air.   her eyes were closed.   her arms were stretched
above her head.   a boy held her wrists together.   the
other five boys stood in a semi-circle in front of the
couch.   the pillow on which her body was pressed
was red.

her breasts were flattened half spheres under her
sweater.   one after the other the five boys leaned
over her and rubbed her breasts.   when the fifth
boy had rubbed them, he went and took her wrists.
the boy who had been holding her wrists went
around to the front of the couch, leaned over and
rubbed her breasts.   the six boys left the room.   the
girl did not move.

House of Anansi Fiction (in print)

Five Legs, *Graeme Gibson*
Korsoniloff, *Matt Cohen*
The Telephone Pole, *Russell Marois*
Eating Out, *John Sandman*
A Perte de Temps, *Pierre Gravel*
The String Box, *Rachel Wyatt*
La Guerre, Yes Sir!, *Roch Carrier*
Victor Victim, *Michael Charters*
The After People, *George Payerle*
The Circuit, *Lawrence Garber*
The Honeyman Festival, *Marian Engel*
Floralie, Where Are You?, *Roch Carrier*
Bartleby, *Chris Scott*
Billy the Kid, *Michael Ondaatje*
When He Was Free And Young And He Used To
    Wear Silks, *Austin Clarke*
Cape Breton Is The Thought Control Centre
    Of Canada, *Ray Smith*
Communion, *Graeme Gibson*
Tales From The Uncertain Country, *Jacques Ferron*
Is It The Sun, Philibert?, *Roch Carrier*
Columbus And The Fat Lady, *Matt Cohen*
No Pain Like This Body, *Harold Sonny Ladoo*